This book
belongs to

This educational book was created in cooperation with Children's Television Workshop, producers of SESAME STREET. Children do not have to watch the television show to benefit from this book. Workshop revenues from this book will be used to help support CTW educational projects.

Featuring the Sesame Street Characters
Children's Television Workshop/Funk & Wagnalls

Authors

Linda Hayward
David Korr
Jeffrey Moss
Michaela Muntean

Illustrators

Tom Brannon
Tom Cooke
Tom Leigh
Kimberly A. McSparran
Sal Murdocca
Anne Sikorski
Maggie Swanson

 Published in the United States of America by Western Publishing Company, Inc., Racine, WI 53404, in conjunction with Children's Television Workshop. Distributed by Funk & Wagnalls, Mahwah, N.J. Manufactured in the United States of America.

0-8343-0075-3

9 0

A Note to Parents

ON MY WAY WITH SESAME STREET is a series designed to help children get off on the right foot. Children feel more comfortable on the path to learning when accompanied by their lovable Sesame Street friends. These 15 volumes are chock-full of favorite stories and activities that reflect the curriculum of the award-winning *Sesame Street* television show.

Each volume covers a different preschool subject:

MY ABC'S
I CAN COUNT
GETTING READY FOR SCHOOL
ANIMALS, ANIMALS
ALL ABOUT ME
COLORS AND SHAPES
PEOPLE IN MY NEIGHBORHOOD
MY FAMILY
CARS AND PLANES, TRUCKS AND TRAINS
UP, DOWN, AND ALL AROUND
MORNING TO NIGHT
JUST PRETEND
IN THE CITY
IN THE COUNTRY
SUMMER, FALL, WINTER, SPRING

A **Parents' Guide** included in each volume helps you and your child get the most out of the book.

With this set, your child will receive a special ON MY WAY WITH SESAME STREET Activity Book. These activities reinforce the educational goals of all 15 books in the series. With colorful stickers, a poster, coloring pages, and a *Going Places* game, these activities will help preschoolers on their way!

A Parents' Guide to MY ABC'S

The first step on the way to reading and writing is learning the alphabet. Children love to sing the alphabet song, but don't always understand that each letter represents a different sound, or that sounds are put together to form words.

The first words that children want to read and write are their own names. Present those letters first. Playing with alphabet blocks or magnetic letters on the refrigerator will help children get a feel for how letters make words.

In "Oscar's Silly ABC's," Oscar offers his Grumpster's Dictionary of Silly Words — from A to Z. F is for flabbergasted and V is for vamoose!

An alphabet chart and loads of activities, including "C is for Cookie," "T is for Telephone," and "Sunday in the Park with Big Bird," help children learn initial letter sounds.

In "Grover's Own Alphabet," children will love learning how the letters of the alphabet are formed.

The alphabet is all around us — not only in books. Read your child "The Mystery of the Missing Muffins" and then see how many things your child can name that begin with the letter M.

We hope that your child will enjoy these stories and activities on the way to mastering alphabet skills.

The Editors
SESAME STREET BOOKS

Oscar's Silly ABC's

Every Grouch should know lots of words for insults, grumbling, and general grouchiness. Grouches also like words that sound silly. The ABC's of grouchery can be found in the official *Grumpster's Dictionary.* In case you don't have a copy in your garbage can, Oscar has selected an alphabet of his favorite grouchy and silly words for you.

abominable Awful; terrible.

The abominable snow monster is not the sort of monster these monsters would like to meet.

bumblebee A flying insect. Some bumblebees sting.

A bumblebee is buzzing around Betty Lou as she picks a bunch of buttercups.

cantankerous Bad-tempered; cranky.

Grouches get very cantankerous when they find flowers growing in their crabgrass gardens.

disgusting Sickening.

Ernie thinks that Oscar's chocolate-covered sardine sundae looks disgusting.

exit To leave. The way out.

A Grouch is an expert at showing visitors the exit.

flabbergasted Very surprised.

glob A lump or pile of something.

Farley is flabbergasted when he sees the glob of mashed turnips on Ferdinand's plate.

hippopotamus A large animal with a big head, short legs, and thick skin.

A hippopotamus will never fit on a bus.

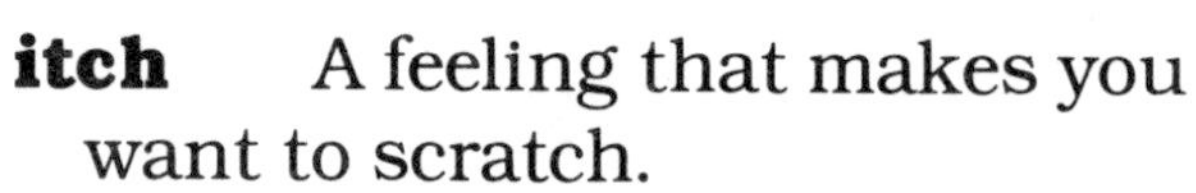

itch A feeling that makes you want to scratch.

Oscar has an itch in the middle of his back.

jiggling An uneven bumping or bouncing motion.

kangaroo An animal that can leap and hop on its back legs. A mother kangaroo carries her baby in a pouch.

The baby kangaroo is jiggling up and down in his mother's pouch.

lollipop A piece of hard candy on a stick.

Leo's lollipop is stuck to his fur.

macaroni A tube-shaped noodle.

Oscar is making macaroni and marshmallows for lunch.

nuisance A pest.

Oscar's nephew, Nestor, makes a nuisance of himself by asking for a new piece of junk every few minutes.

obnoxious Disagreeable; unpleasant.

Oscar is obnoxious when the kids are jumping rope.

porcupine A small animal covered with stiff sharp quills.

Some Grouches like to have porcupines for pets.

quiet Silence; no noise.

If everyone would quit talking, we could have some peace and quiet around here!

rotten Spoiled; stinky.

Stinkweed smells and tastes rotten, and Grouches love it.

scrumptious Very tasty; delicious.

A sardine sandwich on a soggy sesame-seed bun is simply scrumptious!

tickle A light touch that makes you want to laugh.

Ernie is going to tickle Bert with a feather.

ukelele A small four-stringed musical instrument.

vamoose Go away; scram!

I wish you and that ukelele would vamoose!

wiggle To move from side to side.

Oscar's pet worm, Slimey, can wiggle when he walks.

xylophone A musical instrument made of wooden bars and played with two small wooden mallets.

Xavier plays the xylophone at exactly eight o'clock every day.

yo-yo A toy that goes up and down on a string.

The Count is counting how many times Grover's yo-yo is going up and down.

zipper Something that is used to fasten clothes or other things together.

Herry is trying to zip up the zipper on his jacket.

"That's it," Oscar says. "Twenty-six silly words, one for each letter from A to Z. Now it's time for *you* to vamoose! Good-bye, and have a really rotten Grouch day!"

C is for Cookie

The Alphabet Chart

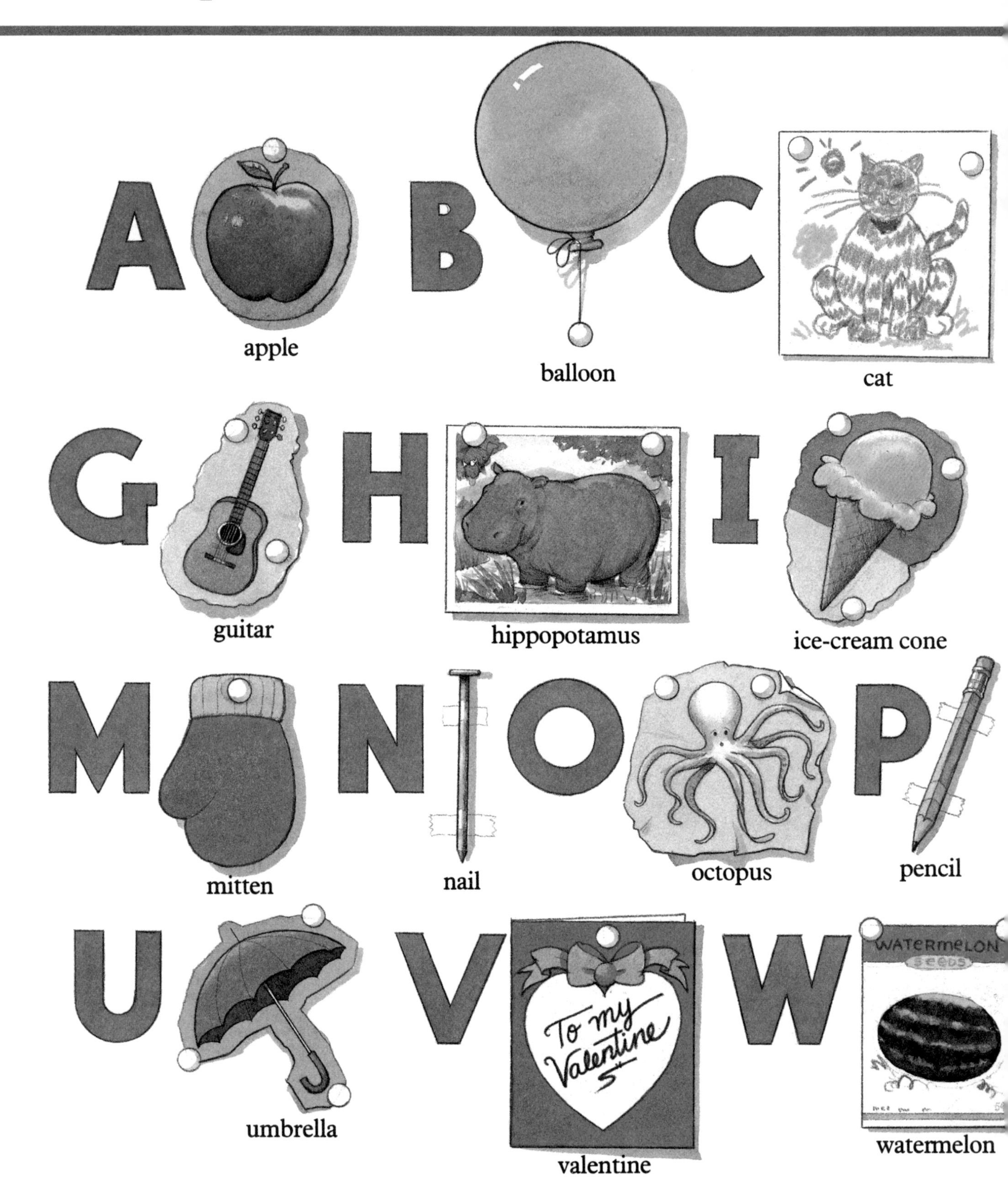

D
dinosaur
E
egg
F
flower
J
jack-in-the-box
K
kangaroo
L
leaf
Q
queen
R
USA
rocket
S
sock
T
television
X
x-ray
Y
yo-yo
Z
zebra

Alphabet Soup

Find all the letters of the alphabet in Cookie Monster's alphabet soup.

E is for Egg
F is for Feather

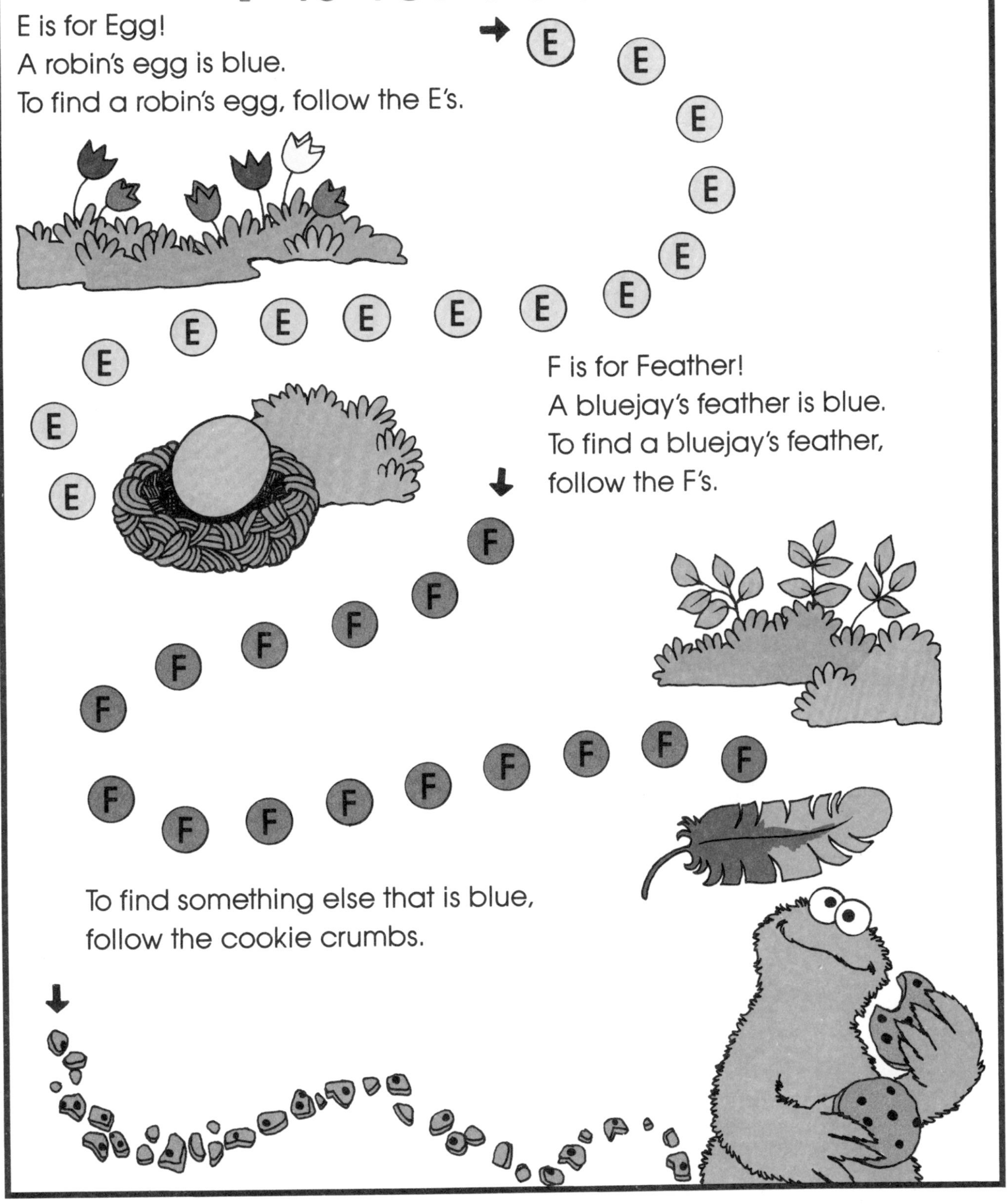

GROVER'S OWN ALPHABET

A

This is a little awkward, but is it not an absolutely adorable A?

D

It is not such a big deal to do a D! It is delightful!

E

I have to bend my elbow exactly right, but how is this for an elegant E? EEEK!

B

I bet you think making this big beautiful B with my furry little body is easy. Well, it is not!

C

And now I am making you a *cute* letter C! But I am not very comfortable.

F

Here is a funny, furry F for you!

G

G is for GROVER! Watch while I, Grover, form the great letter G! Am I not graceful?

H

I hope this H makes you happy. It is hard to do (pant, pant)! Help!

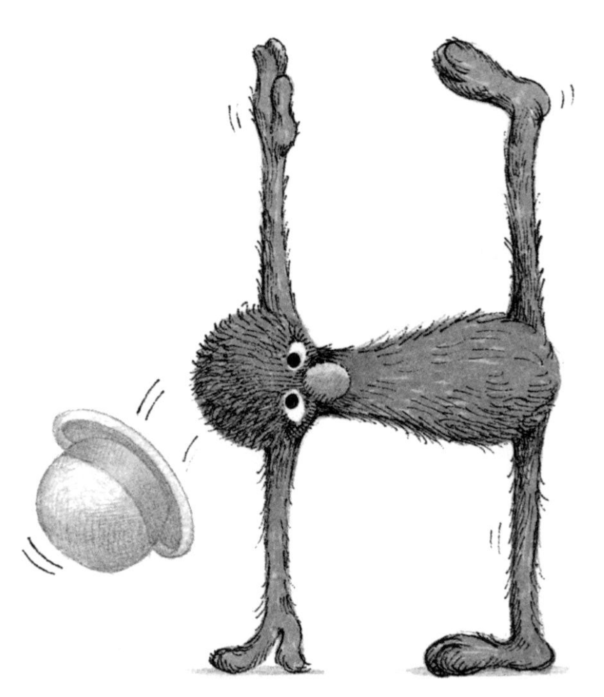

I

It is I, Grover, making the important letter I.

L

I do not like to be lazy about this, but the lovely letter L takes very little work.

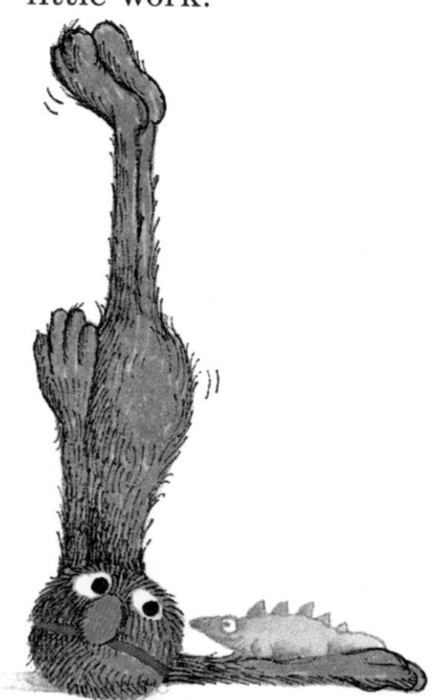

M

Isn't this a magnificent M? It is made by ME!

J

Now (puff, puff!) I am juggling just to show you a J. I could get in a jam this way.

K

This is the letter K. I am not kidding.

N

I thought we would *never* get to the nifty letter N!

O

Oh, my goodness (glub, glub)! I am not the only one in this ocean.

P

What is the point of my standing like this? I am pretending to be the letter P.

Q

Quick! Answer this question! What letter am I now? Q? Oh, thank goodness you guessed it.

T

I have tried to make a *terrific* T for you! But, oh, I am so tired. TA-DA!

U

I would undergo anything to show you the letter U.

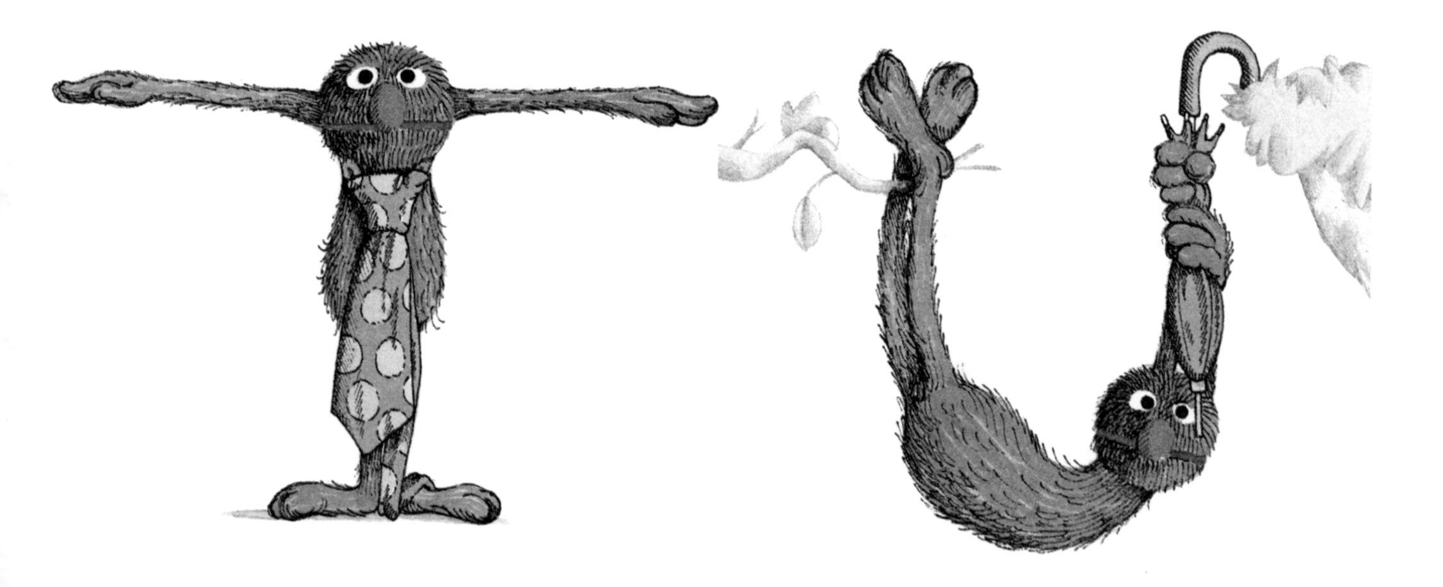

R

You want an R? All *right!!* Here you are (pant, pant)! This is getting ridiculous!

S

So sorry. I couldn't find a single thing to assist me with this S. I simply had to use my *self.*

V

You are invited to view my very valuable letter V.

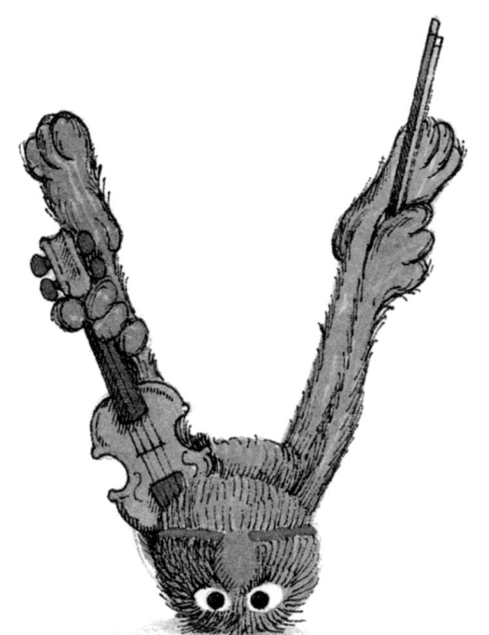

W

I wish you would watch my wonderful diving W.

X

And how about this extraordinary X? Oh, I am so excited!

You, yes, you asked for it — the letter Y. *Yikes!*

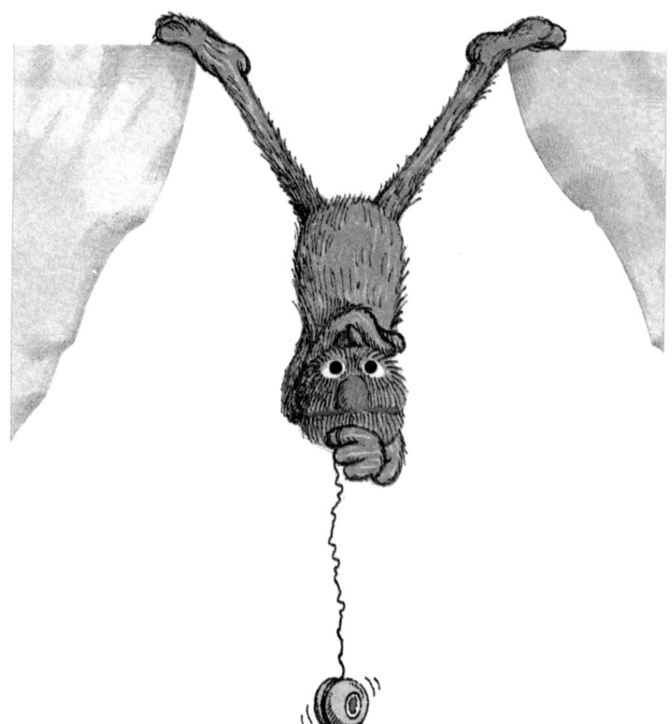

Z

Here it is (puff, puff!), the last letter — Z! Did you like the way I zipped through the entire alphabet?

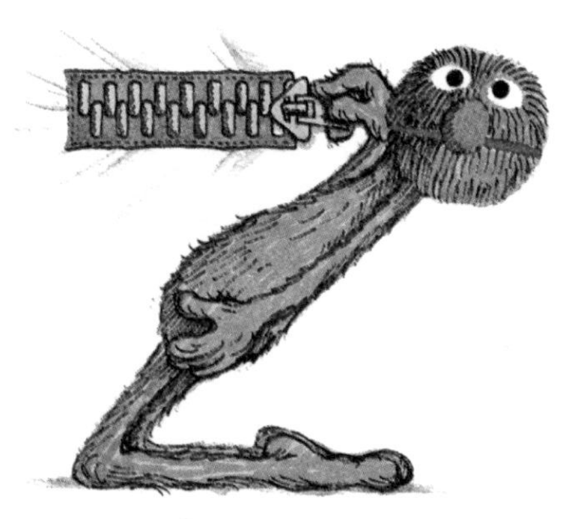

This is not a letter of the alphabet. This is a tired monster!

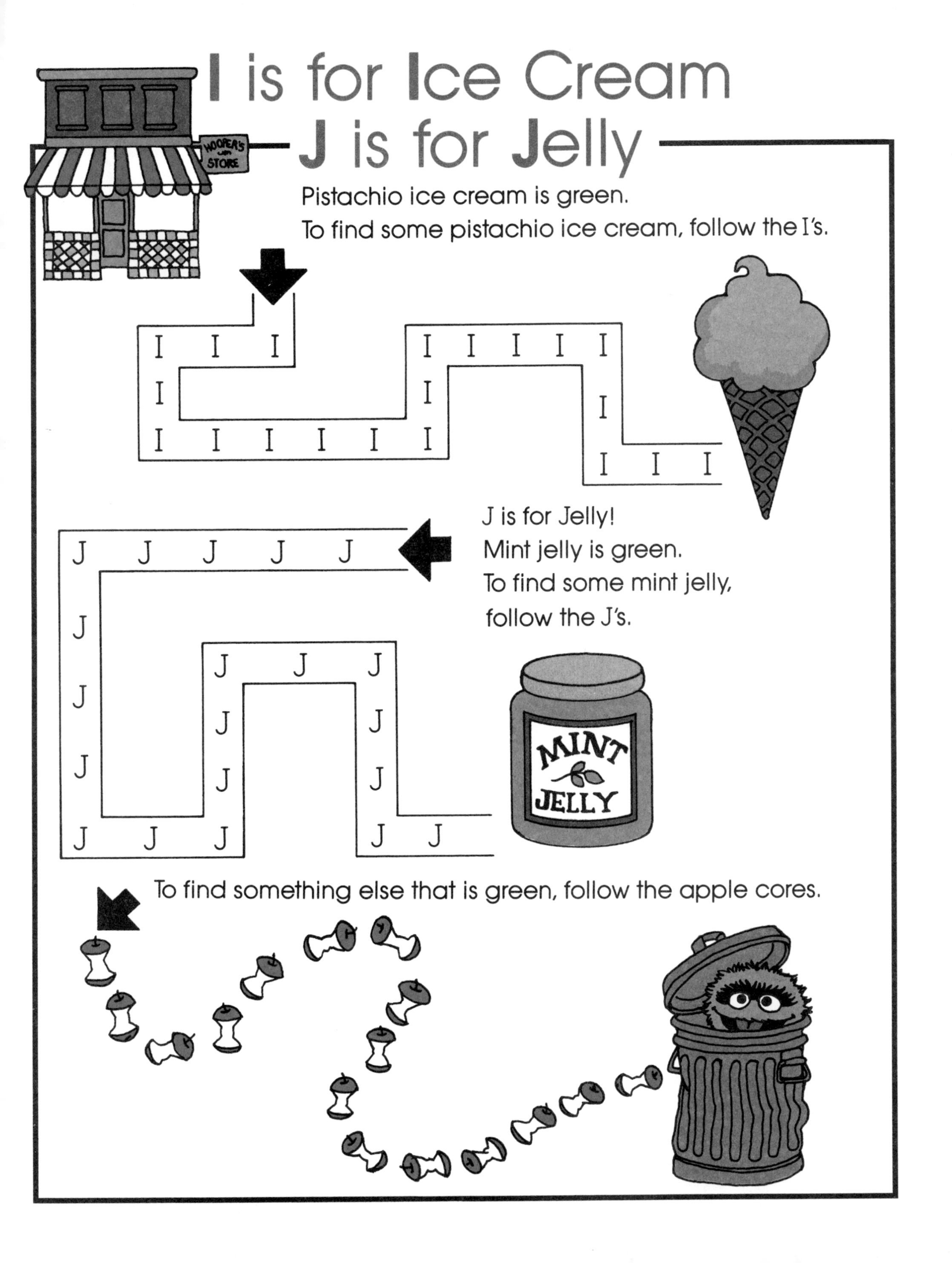
I is for Ice Cream
J is for Jelly
HOOPER'S STORE
Pistachio ice cream is green.
To find some pistachio ice cream, follow the I's.
J is for Jelly!
Mint jelly is green.
To find some mint jelly,
follow the J's.
MINT JELLY
To find something else that is green, follow the apple cores.

The Mystery of the Missing Muffins

One Monday morning, I, Sherlock Hemlock, the world's greatest detective, went to Mr. and Mrs. Mopple's Market on Mulberry Street to get some muffins and marmalade. I marched past the milk, the melons, the mustard and the maple syrup to the muffin shelf. But much to my amazement there weren't any muffins.

"I came for muffins and marmalade," I said. "But there aren't any muffins."

"Mercy me," said Mr. Mopple. "There was a multitude of muffins there only minutes ago."

"Egad," I said. "The muffins were here and now they aren't. Most mysterious." I looked through my magnifying glass at the place where the missing muffins had been. "Maybe," I said, "you mailed the muffins by mistake. Or a mean magician turned the muffins into marbles, and they rolled away. Or perhaps a million mice made off with the muffins, because they want them for mattresses. Muffins make good mouse mattresses."

But Mr. and Mrs. Mopple hadn't been to the mailbox to mail anything that morning, and they hadn't seen any magicians or marbles or mice, either. So I, Sherlock Hemlock, thought some more.

"Just a moment," I said. "Magpies and monkeys like muffins. Have you seen any magpies or monkeys?"

Mr. and Mrs. Mopple shook their heads.

"What about moles or mallards or mules?" I asked. "They might like muffins."

But they hadn't seen any of them, either. What a muddle!

Then Mrs. Mopple said, "You might ask Marvin Monster, who works for us."

So I went to talk to Marvin Monster. "Marvin," I said, "have you been to the mailbox to mail anything this morning? Or have you seen any magicians or marbles or mice or moles or mallards or magpies or monkeys?"

"No, sir," said Marvin, who was a most well-mannered monster.

Now I was more mixed-up than ever. So I decided to go home and mull over the mystery. But as I made my way past the mushrooms, the mayonnaise and the marshmallows, there — piled right next to the marmalade – were the missing muffins.

"Eureka!" I shouted.

Mr. and Mrs. Mopple and Marvin Monster came running.

"I found the muffins," I told them. "They're right here next to the marmalade."

"Of course," said Marvin Monster. "I moved them there myself. I think muffins go well with marmalade, don't you, Mr. Hemlock?"

"Zounds! Why didn't you tell me, Marvin?"

"You didn't ask me about the muffins, Mr. Hemlock," murmured Marvin. "You asked me if I had been to the mailbox, or seen any magicians or marbles or mice, or mallards or magpies or monkeys."

Feeling merry now that the Mystery of the Missing Muffins was but a memory, I went home to munch on muffins and marmalade – and they did go very well together indeed.

T is for Telephone

Betty Lou is inviting a friend to come over and play.
Who is Betty Lou calling?
Put your finger on Betty Lou's telephone.
Now follow the wire until you come to another telephone.
The Count's pet cat is caught in a tree. Who is the Count calling?
Mr. Snuffle-upagus is inviting his best friend over for spaghetti.
Who is Snuffie calling?

My ABC's

Big Bird found the letter A. Find some other letters of the alphabet hidden in the picture below.

OSCAR-THE-GROUCH'S
ALPHABET OF TRASH

A is for Alphabet.

B is for Busted Balloon. That's the best kind! Heh, heh!

C is for Can. Here's my rusty can collection. Isn't it beautiful?

D is for Dust. It's time to dust my furniture.
E is for Eggshells. I always put some in my bed at night to get a crummy night's sleep.
F is for Fishbones, and G is for Garbage. Here's the Garbage Grouch now, with my weekly supply.

H is for Hat. How do you like my horrible hat?
I is for Ice Cream. Ice Cream is icky — except when it has pickles and sardines on top.
J is for my Junky Jack-in-the-box. I broke this one when I was just a little grouch.
K is for Kite. I fly kites only if I can get them caught in trees.
L is for Ladder. Luckily, the rungs on this ladder are broken, so I can't get my kite down.

M is for Mangled Mirror. I managed to mash mine in all the right places.

N is for my No-good Necktie. It helped me win the Worst-Dressed Grouch of the Year award.

O is for the only good thing that starts with O — Oscar!

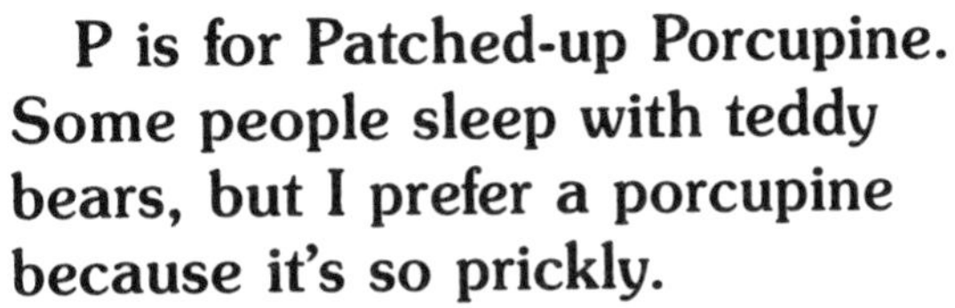

P is for Patched-up Porcupine. Some people sleep with teddy bears, but I prefer a porcupine because it's so prickly.

Q is for Quilt. I've had this quilt since I was just a baby Grouch.

R is for Rotten Rubbers that I sometimes wear in the rain, which reminds me of my two favorite S words — Soaked Socks!

T is for Taxi. It's terrific when one splashes you.

U is for my Ugly Umbrella.

V is for Violin. I love to play the Grouch Sonata late at night. It's a very good way to get lots of valuable trash! Heh, heh!
SCREECH!
W is for Worm. I now present my pet, Slimey, the wonderful waltzing worm!
X is for X-ray pictures. This is my famous exhibit of X-ray pictures.
COOKIE MONSTER
OSCAR-THE-GROUCH
SAM THE ROBOT
GOAT

Y is for my Yucchy Yellow Yo-Yo.
Z is for Zigzag Zippers. I love old zippers because they're always getting stuck.

There! That's my alphabet of trash — from A to Z! Now, go away!

Find the A's and Z's

Letters Make Words

The words we say are made of sounds.
The words we read are made of letters.
Here are some of our favorite words!

What is your favorite word?

Sunday in the Park with Big Bird

ABCDEFGHIJKLMN

Find something in the picture that begins with each letter of the alphabet.

O P Q R S T U V W X Y Z

CTW
SESAME STREET®